ARTWORK – CONCEPT AND PENCIL: GIANLUCA BARONE   COLORS: DARIO CALABRIA   INK: SANTA ZANGARI

2

TO DISTRACT THE **RANGERS**, GRUUMM SENT A FORCE OF BLUEHEADS AND KRYBOTS TO **ATTACK** S.P.D.'S DELTA BASE...

HOLD THEM OFF, RANGERS! THEY CAN KNOCK, BUT THEY **CAN'T** COME IN!

...WHILE **INSIDE** DELTA BASE, KAT LEARNED OF MORE TROUBLE.

SEND THE OMEGA RANGER ON THE **OMEGAMAX CYCLE!**

SIR, A **LARGE** ROBOT IS ATTACKING THE **OTHER SIDE** OF THE CITY...

WITH THE **OMEGA RANGER** AT ITS CONTROLS, S.P.D.'S QUICKEST ZORD **RACED** ACROSS THE CITY...

VVVRRAAMMM!

5

6

8

THE SHIELD OF HOPE

A VERY LONG TIME AGO, A MAGIC DRAGON USED ITS FIERY BREATH AND SCALES FROM ITS BODY TO CREATE TWO ENCHANTED BATTLE SHIELDS – *THE SHIELD OF DARKNESS* AND *THE SHIELD OF HOPE!*

ROAAARRRRR!

EVIL KORAGG NOW HAD THE SHIELD OF DARKNESS, BUT TO THIS DAY, THE SHIELD OF HOPE HAD NEVER BEEN FOUND...

ARTWORK – CONCEPT AND PENCIL: GIANLUCA BARONE   COLORS: DARIO CALABRIA   INK: MICHELA FRARE

IN THE MYSTIC FOREST, DAGGERON TOLD THE MYSTIC RANGERS WHY...

TO PROTECT THE SHIELD FROM EVIL, IT WAS HIDDEN IN A DENSE FOREST LABYRINTH.

ONLY THE PURE OF HEART CAN SEE THE LABYRINTH'S ENTRANCE, BUT EVEN THEY CAN'T FIND THEIR WAY THROUGH IT.

LEAVING TO COLLECT SUPPLIES, NICK COULDN'T GET DAGGERON'S TALE OUT OF HIS MIND...

THAT SHIELD COULD BE A USEFUL WEAPON IN OUR FIGHT AGAINST EVIL.

WE *CAN'T* GIVE UP ON FINDING IT - *WHOA!*

12

14

15

FROM SIRIUS, WITH MENACE

FFFUMP-DOOOSHH!

TRACKED BY S.P.D.'S HEADQUARTERS AS IT HURTLED DOWN THROUGH EARTH'S ATMOSPHERE, A *MYSTERIOUS* SPACE CAPSULE SPLASHED INTO THE SEA OFF NEWTECH CITY'S COASTLINE...

ARTWORK – CONCEPT AND PENCIL: LUCIO LEONI   COLORS: DARIO CALABRIA   INK: OSCAR SCALCO

19

21

AFTER MORPHING INTO THE SHADOW RANGER, CRUGER SPED TO THE SCENE ON THE ATV...

TENTILLAS CAN PICK UP THE SCENT OF MY SIRIAN BLOOD FROM HUGE DISTANCES...

YES! IT'S COMING AFTER ME!

SHADOW RANGER TO MEGAZORD - WHEN YOU'RE FREE, BLAST IT WITH EVERYTHING YOU'VE GOT!

BUT IN THE MEGAZORD COCKPIT...

EVERYTHING'S BEEN DAMAGED BY THE CRUSHING TENTACLES!

ALL WEAPONS SYSTEMS ARE DOWN!

A HUGE TENTACLE THEN WHIPPED INTO THE ATV...

NOOOO!

ROLLING TO HIS FEET, THE RANGER REACHED FOR HIS SHADOW SABER...

ALL RIGHT, THIS IS GOING TO GET NASTY!

THE GIANT TENTILLA COILED MORE TENTACLES, READY TO STRIKE...